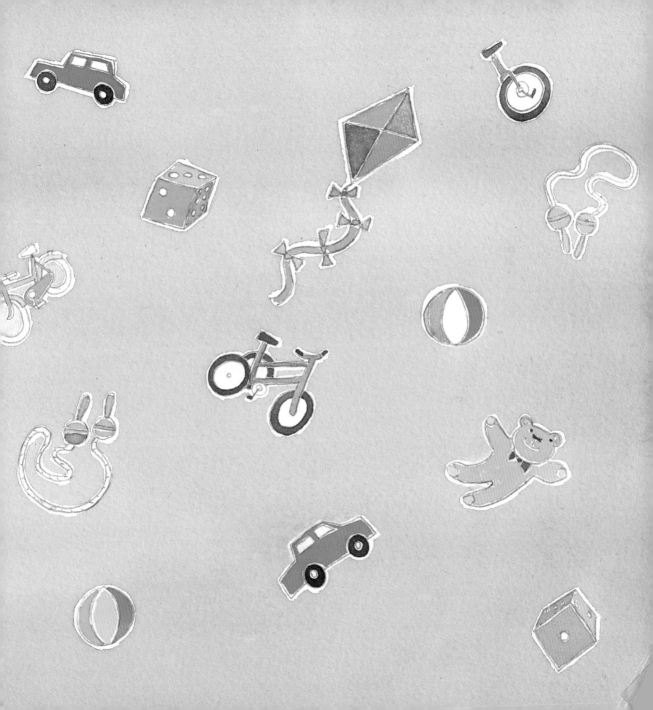

For Rose Dodd. E.D.

Copyright © 1999 Zero to Ten Limited
Illustrations copyright © 1999 Emma Dodd • Text copyright © 1999 Hannah Reidy

Publisher: Anna McQuinn • Art Director: Tim Foster
Senior Art Editor: Sarah Godwin • Senior Editor: Simona Sideri
First published in Great Britain in hard cover in 1999 by Zero to Ten Limited.
This edition published in 2000 by Zero to Ten Limited
327 High Street, Slough, Berkshire SL1 1TX

ISBN 1-84089-187-4

Printed in Hong Kong.

How **many** can you see?

Written by Hannah Reidy
Illustrated by Emma Dodd

On the pavement, in the sun
Una is skipping, having fun...

On her own,
"One, one one!"

Over at the school yard
when it's fine,
lots of children play in line.

In they go, **two by two...**

... now there's only Shane and Hugh...

... just **two!**

By the trees, in the breeze children racing, all on wheels!

Austin's **first**

Bel's in the **middle**

and **last** is Celie

who's doing
a wheelie!

Early in the morning,
on the sands, Leah and Lilly
holding hands...

Fly their kites, **one**, **two**,
If you had a best friend
wouldn't you?

In the middle of the day
when the sun is hot
crowds of children playing,
what a **lot!**

Josh and Jane,
    have got a new game.

They play all the time
    even in the rain!

Giant dice! Isn't that nice –
one hop, **two** hop,
    that makes twice!

Dad should
go and take
a peep...

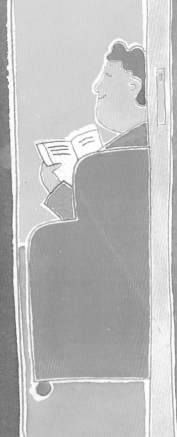

In Between Books

Hannah Reidy and Emma Dodd

"... a delight; every single word has been chosen by Hannah Reidy with tender loving care..."
THE GUARDIAN

"Bridge the gap between first-word books and simple story books..."
JUNIOR MAGAZINE

"... I didn't think it was possible to have a new slant on early counting — but here it is... it's all much too attractive!"
THE GUARDIAN

What do you like to Wear? 1-84089-184-X
What Noises can you Hear? 1-84089-185-8
What does it Look like? 1-84089-186-6
How Many can you See? 1-84089-187-4

All available in paperback at £4.50
Also available in hardcover at £5.99

Crazy Creature Concepts

Hannah Reidy and Clare Mackie

If you enjoyed the **In Between Series**, you will love these titles, also by Hannah Reidy

"...introducing concepts in an inspiring way."
THE GOOD BOOK GUIDE

"...inspired alliterative text and zany illustrations provide an introduction to numbers and suggest that language can be enormous fun."
TIME OUT

Crazy Creature Colours 1-84089-069-X
Crazy Creature Counting 1-84089- 070-3
Crazy Creature Capers 1-84089- 071-1
Crazy Creature Contrasts 1-84089-072-X

All available in paperback at £4.50

Also from ZERO TO TEN
Where's Everybody Going?
Quentin Samuel and Christopher Corr

Some people have bikes, some are going by bus, Stevie has a little car, Kirsty B has a limo, Mike has a truck, Jade has a van, Jeff has a convertible and Alice has a jeep... but where's everybody going?

ISBN: 1-84089-126-2, hardcover £6.99

ZERO TO TEN books are available from all good bookstores.
If you have problems obtaining any title, please contact the publishers:

Zero to Ten Limited
327 High Street, Slough
Berks, SL1 1TX

Tel: 01753 578 499
Fax: 01753 578 488

can you see?

How **many**

Rachel is having
one last bounce before
she goes to sleep!